Shonette and Amy

Rudolph's Brother Fred and the Mischievous Gnome

(Tune of: Nellie The Elephant)

To Lapland
A herd of reindeer came
One of them was bright red
And Fred was his name!
(SHOUT OUT: He was Rudolph's Brother!)
One cold night
He slipped out of the shed
Sick of being a reindeer
He went to paint your town RED!

Chorus -

Fred the Reindeer, packed his bag
And said Goodbye to the Sleigh Gang!
Off he went with clippotty clop,
Clop,clop,clop
Fred the Reindeer, packed his bag
And went to paint your town!
Off he went with a clippotty clop,
Clop, clop, clop!

In the Grotto
The Mischievous Gnome played
He was fed up and bored
And mischief was his game!
The same cold night
Out of the grotto he tread
Bumping into a reindeer
And that Reindeer was... FRED!
(SHOUT OUT: Rudolph's Brother!)

'To do' list:
- Polish boots
- Clean sleigh
- Feed reindeers
- Finish wrapping
- Pack passport
- REMEMBER magic key

Santa's good list:
Paddy
Mara
Dougie
Millie
Harry
Molly
Shonette
George
Sofia
Ana Lucia
Theo
Tommy
Norah
Danny
Lily
Maya

Ben

Jo

Lola

Tom

Chorus -

Fred the Reindeer, packed his bag
And said Goodbye to the Sleigh Gang!
Off he went with clippotty clop,
Clop,clop,clop
Fred the Reindeer, packed his bag
And went to paint your town!
Off he went with a clippotty clop,
Clop, clop, clop!

In your town
The Mischievous Gnome and Fred came
(whisper - Rudolph's Brother!)
They purchased 15 cans of paint
And brushes they bought the same!
That cold night
They painted everywhere
They got totally carried away
They even painted their hair!

RED x15

RED

clippotty
clop

Chorus -

Fred the Reindeer, packed his bag
And said Goodbye to the Sleigh Gang!
Off he went with clippotty clop,
Clop,clop,clop
Fred the Reindeer, packed his bag
And went to paint your town!
Off he went with a clippotty clop,
Clop, clop, clop!

Just in time
Father Christmas came
He made them paint it back again
BUT your town will never be the same!
Look everywhere
Can you see the red?
Be very careful or you might
get some on your head!!
(Throw red silly string or
paper on the reader!)

Chorus -

Fred the Reindeer, packed his bag
And said Goodbye to the Sleigh Gang!
Off he went with clippotty clop,
Clop,clop,clop
Fred the Reindeer, packed his bag
And went to paint your town!
Off he went with a clippotty clop,
Clop, clop, clop!

• •

(Name of the school, setting or child).

**Wish you a very Merry Christmas
We hope you have a lovely time and get
many Christmas wishes.**

The END